EVIL EMPEROR PENGUIN

THE WORLD WILL BE MINE!

LAURA ELLEN ANDERSON

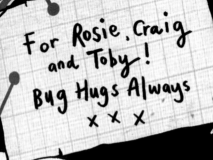

For Rosie, Craig
and Toby!
Bug Hugs Always
x x x

The comics in this book were originally published as
Evil Emperor Penguin (Almost) Takes Over The World! and *Evil Emperor Penguin: Winging It!*

Adaptation, additional artwork and colour by Kate Brown.
Cover design by Laura Ellen Anderson and Paul Duffield.

Evil Emperor Penguin: The World Will Be Mine! is a
DAVID FICKLING BOOK

First published in Great Britain in 2023 by
David Fickling Books,
31 Beaumont Street,
Oxford, OX1 2NP

MIX
Paper from
responsible sources
FSC® C007785

DAVID FICKLING BOOKS Reg. No. 8340307

A CIP catalogue record for this book is available from the British Library.

Printed in Great Britain by Bell & Bain Ltd, Glasgow.

QUANTUM EEP

Number 8, you radish. Have you finished making my newest evil invention yet?!

Yes, sir, just installed the evil flusher...

This is most definitely my key to world domination!

I've been wanting to try this invention for years!

So, here it is, sir...

The ultimate *Time Toilet!*

Perfect, Number 8! And nobody will ever suspect this is a time machine when they see it!

So this is the plan, Number 8!

I will travel back to every important date in history!

I will win all the battles, I will find the cure for the plagues. I will invent *everything* that was ever invented!

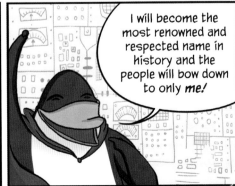

I will become the most renowned and respected name in history and the people will bow down to only *me!*

7

Eugene, you'll be mission control. And you, the other one, you can help Eugene.

Me! Neill! I love helping!

I don't care.

You enter the chosen date, and the location, then the toilet will be flushed three times...

You pull the lever on the *third* flush.

Can I press this red button?

It's *very* important that you only pull the lever during the *third flush.*

What happens if it's pulled before or after?

I haven't worked that out yet, so perhaps it's a good idea to just avoid doing it.

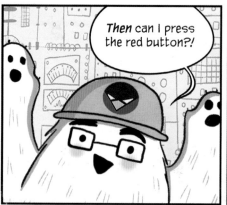

Then can I press the red button?!

Can someone recycle him, or something?

Who *are* you again?

It's me, Neill!

Yay for Neill!

Yay for me!

Number 8, fetch me a mop so I can poke them.

We're wasting time, there's no time to lose! We have time to alter...

Where are you planning on travelling to first, sir?

Hmmm, maybe one to two million years ago when humans first discovered fire...

Or 3500^{BC} when the wheel was invented...

Maybe we should pick something more recent, just to make sure the Time Toilet runs smoothly.

What's the point of a time machine if it can't travel back that far?!

I'm not saying it can't. It's just safer to check that it works well first.

We don't want to end up stuck in the Paleolithic.

We could always go back to 1886, when Josephine Cochrane invented the dishwasher.

If you were remembered for that, you would become a true hero!

A dishwasher? Are you actually serious?

I could save the *Titanic* from hitting the iceberg and sinking, or I could split the atom... and you choose the invention of the *dishwasher*?

I thought it was quite an impressive invention.

Fine, *you* go back and *marry* the dishwasher and have tiny, squeaky clean dish babies!

I've decided to pick 1687...

Yay! I love 1687!

Step aside Newton... Evil Emperor Penguin shall soon be remembered for formulating the three laws of motion!

Ooo, ooo! I know the three laws of motion!

It's sit, stand and snuggle, right?!

No, Neill, you silly Billy. It's stop, drop and roll...

Oh, really?

10

11

13

I wouldn't recommend drawing attention to us, sir...

Heeeeey, friends!

No... no... We're not your friends. We are enemies. As you were... Go away!

We should go back into the Time Toilet and leave, sir. If we speak to our past selves, we risk changing the future!

And any mistake we make in the past could have catastrophic effects on the present day!

Everyone's our friend! We are all one big happy family of frieeeends!

Let's sing!

He's singing Kumbaya... I have *never* sung Kumbaya.

That can *not* be me in the past!

I am baffled, sir. How did you go from that... to a megalomaniac?

FLUSH

Hey! Who's the in the Time Toilet?!

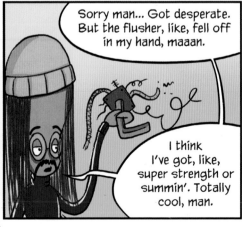

Sorry man... Got desperate. But the flusher, like, fell off in my hand, maaan.

I think I've got, like, super strength or summin'. Totally cool, man.

14

15

Pish posh, beautiful schmootiful. World domination is your path. Face it. Done.

Pahahaha! You're hilarious! Prince 8, these guys are funny!

It wasn't a joke. Stop aggressively dancing at me.

So, have you read many books? Or considered university?

Why would I do that? I'm a prince, maaan. I don't need to read books or study. I'm a free spirit!

Number 8, I need to teach past-me to be evil!

And I need to teach past-me how to be clever...

How on earth were we ever so different to now?!

If our past-selves don't learn to be evil, then the present-us will be...

nice.

Well, we'd better do something quickly! I'm hugging myself!

16

That night...

...And that's when I decided I wanted to help people and bring peace and harmony to the world.

Boring!

I always wanted to play the tambourine.

Did you? Did you *really?*

Haven't you ever wondered what it would be like to *rule* the world?!

Hmm...

And eat spaghetti hoops whenever you liked?!

Have you ever wondered what it would be like to study some rocket science? Astrophysics? Build evil inventions?!

I study peace, maaan.

Oh boy.

Try these... I brought a spare tin with me.

They're very hoopy, for food...

What are they?

Your new favourite thing...

17

UM NUM NUM

They're *DELICIOUS!!!*

More! *MORE!*

Okay, now we're getting somewhere.

Just have a try... It's full of great facts!

Ergh, fine, man. But books make me sleepy.

Really HARD FACTS AND intelligent STUFF

Next morning...

Wow! I never knew quantum theory was so interesting... and easy!

I heart spaghetti hoops.

Y'know, I think I know how to improve that poncho of yours...

Really? But I like it how it is...

SNIP SNIP SNIP

SNIP

SNIP

18

20

But it's kind of tricky when your arms have disappeared...

Sir, we've fixed the flusher... The Time Toilet should be back in working order now!

Excellent! Now we can go back home!

TIME TOILET NUMBER 2

Eugene, come in, are you there?

Oh yay! We couldn't find you anywhere, Mister 8!

The Time Toilet was broken for a while, but we're all fixed now!

Who's that down the toilet? He sounds so cute!

Oh, that's Eugene.

Can I say hi?!

Err... sure.

Oh, hello, Eugene! My name is Ernest!

Ooo! I love the name Ernest!!!

We could have a big bowl of spaghetti hoops together!

And talk about unicorns!

I love unicorns!!!

Okay, that's enough! Firstly, you do *not* love unicorns...

And secondly, I have to leave *now*! Eugene, get the present-day settings ready!

It's been so lovely meeting you! And Eugene seems delightful!

I'd love to meet him properly one day!

Yes, well, that depends...

Number 8, it's no good. Past-EEP is too nice! I'm going to end up as...

Good Emperor Penguin. And Eugene won't exist!

Hmmm... I may have an idea.

Here... a little parting gift. Don't open it until we're gone!

Why, thank you!

What do you mean, you 'can't right now'?! Just hit present day and pull the lever!

Or are you incapable of following my orders?

Oh, no, Evil Master... It's just a little hard because I lost my arms.

And I think my leg has started to disappear too...

That's the worst excuse I've ever heard, Eugene...

Body parts don't just randomly go missing!

Sir! What if he's right...?

This is what I was warning you about earlier. If the past-you doesn't want to rule the world...

...then he'll never create the abominable snowman minion clones...

There will be no minions... Eugene is disappearing from existence entirely!

Hey, it's me, Neill! Sending you back now!

Present day, EEP HQ

Eugene! Oh no! Your legs have completely gone!

Oh, hi, Evil Master and Mister 8! I'm waving, but you can't see that...

24

I think us minions are gaining the power of invisibility!

It's me, Neill! I lost my head!

Number 8! You said that envelope would work!

Not for sure. Give it time...

We don't **have** time! Eugene has almost faded away!

Yay! I'm fading!

And me! It's me, Neill!

Don't worry, Evil Master, I'll reappear again...

Won't I?

POP!

Eugene...?

EUGENE!?!

Oh, what's wrong, Evil Master?

Don't be sad...

Eugene!

I mean... ahem. Don't you dare go disappearing like that again!

I'm here too, Evil Master!

Who are you again?

It's me, Neill!

Oh, you didn't have to reappear, it's fine.

27

Number 8! Why are there *potatoes* connected to my evil invention?

The devices we already have won't provide enough electricity, sir.

And potatoes *will?!*

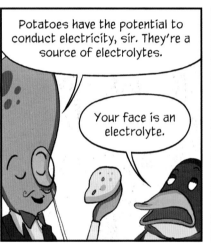

Potatoes have the potential to conduct electricity, sir. They're a source of electrolytes.

Your face is an electrolyte.

The electrolytes act as an electrical conductor, meaning they allow the flow of electric charge.

The potatoes will provide that extra push to make the invention work perfectly, sir!

You baffle me, Number 8...

This is going to be my best invention yet!

By connecting all of our electronic devices... and potatoes, and then turning them all on at once, enough energy will be created to form a portal to space!

All the world leaders will get sucked into the portal, off into space, and I shall rule this whole planet myself!

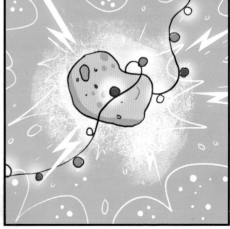

30

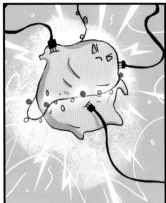

Is that... a potato... with abs?

I... I don't know what to say, sir.

How do you know if that's the look of a potato who's angry?

Or who has trapped wind?

But look at how pretty he looks with all those fairy lights!

Oh, look, he just punched the floor and cracked it...

I'm thinking perhaps we should run, Evil Master?

How did my evil portal turn into a potato monster?!

SMASH!

Well, I don't think it's here to be spuddy-spuddy with us!

This is all your fault, Number 8, for suggesting we use stupid potatoes!

I didn't know it would create a potato monster, sir...

We need to think of a way to stop it...

How does one defeat a huge potato monster?

Maybe we could eat it?

That's *morbid*, Eugene. I like it.

Cutlery at the ready!

CLANK

It's *time to dine!!!*

ZZZPP!

Okay! Electric potato! It's an *electric potato monster!*

Time to run again!

I, Evil Cat, your most handsome arch-nemesis, have come destroy you! mwahahaaaar–

Oh, for crying out loud... *Not you!*

Oh, I'm sorry... is this a bad time?

It's always a bad time when it concerns you, Evil Cat!

Oh, well, that is rather hurtful...

Also, in case you hadn't noticed, I'm being hunted by a *giant electric potato! With abs!*

Eleven abs! That's not natural!

Oh, come on, how can you be threatened by a potato?!

Look, it's just a big, harmless, mutated vegetable...

Hey, Tattie, I'm Evil Cat. How's it go—

ZZP

RAAARGH!!!

ZZP

ZZP

ZZP

Okay! It clearly doesn't want to chat...

Quick! I know somewhere we can hide! Follow me to my room!

Eugene... what is this abomination we're sitting in?

My Unicorn-Magic Cloud Castle. Keith bought it for me last Christmas...

The potato monster will never find us in here!

Clearly, it doesn't know how to use a door!

I can't believe we're being hunted by a carnivorous vegetable...

At least we're safe in here...

OOO, UNICORN-MAGIC CLOUD CASTLE!!!

What?!

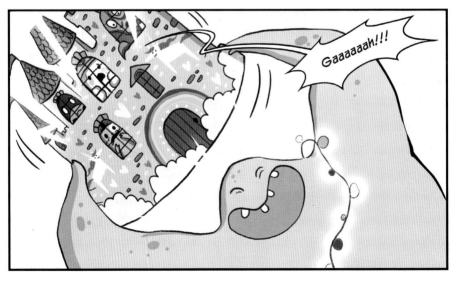

Gaaaaaah!!!

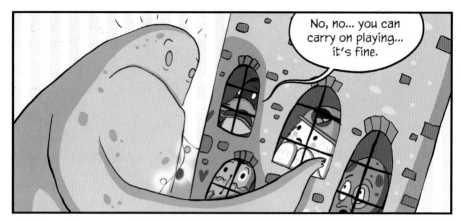

No, no... you can carry on playing... it's fine.

ZZZP

CRACK

SMASH

CRRK

SNAP

ZZP

How has he broken my castle?!

It's made of unbreakable unicorn-glitter glue!

It's getting more powerful!

Why don't we head for the Kitchen of Evil?!

We might be able to lure the potato monster into the kitchen oven...

...and bake it!

It bakes normal potatoes perfectly well, so surely it could bake an evil one!

I don't think this potato can be lured!

The baking plan isn't going to work!

We're potato pie!

SNFFFF

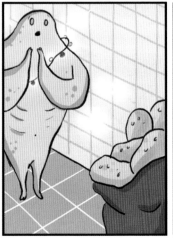

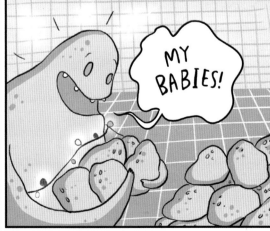

MY BABIES!

37

It's found the spare potatoes...

BABIES COME HOME!

Wow. It took every single potato...

Saved from a potato, by potatoes...

Where did the pram come from?

That night...

So, do I get to lava your face now?

Are you still here?!

Wait, how rude of me... I'll let you finish your dinner first.

Look at all these pretty shoes!

No wonder the humans love them so much...

How do you chooooose?!

I like that one because it makes you look like you're on tippy toes!

I like the ones with sparkles...

You like anything that sparkles, Neill!

Minions! You sound like you're having fun! Stop it!

This 'Shoe World' brochure got caught in the post interceptor, Evil Master!

Give me that!

See ya, Eugene!

Yeah, bye!

'Each beautifully hand-crafted shoe, is made unique like you...'

Well, first of all, that's stupid...

And secondly, I have the perfect plan, Eugene!

Ooo, what is it?

We're going to make our very own brand of shoes!

Once the human puts the shoes on – they'll never come off, and they'll be programmed to walk the human straight into my trap!

I shall call them 'Shoe-per Shoes!'

Over a million pairs made so far, Eugene! We should probably check they actually work...

And you shall be my test subject, of course.

I'd be honoured, Evil Master!

I am ready to test the Shoe-per Shoes, Evil Master!

And I tied the laces all by myself!

My Shoe-per Shonic Shoe Tracker will pinpoint exactly where you are located...

Then I can activate the Shoe-per Shoe to start walking from where you are, straight to me!

I'll be waiting with bells on and a big fat human trap.

La la laaaah!

Hey there! I'm a test subject. Who are you?

AIRY PLANES

Okay, Eugene is right on course.

Once he arrives at the North Pole, I'll activate the Shoe-per Shoes!

NORTH POLE

Hey, Evil Master! Look! The North Pole! I'm here, I am!

NORTH POLE

Prepare to lose control of your feet in 3...2...1...

Eugene, are they working?

Ooo! I'm walking without trying! They work, Evil Master!

KZZZCHH!

CLINK

KZZZCHH!

CLINK

Um, Evil Master? I'm heading towards some water...

Yes, I can see that, Eugene...

Um... okay, Evil Master...

Evil Master, I'm scared!

42

43

45

BIG FAT DOOM BUTTON

Well, Eugene. Make yourself at home, because you won't be leaving.

Ever again.

And don't think I've forgotten about your little secret red button that you keep hidden in your hat...

Y'know, the one that summons unicorns who chase me for several *days!*

I shall be confiscating it, then *destroying* it! Oh, and I've also created an anti-unicorn forcefield around my evil base, so your buddy Keith will never be able to save you!

And quite frankly, I'm *sick* of those sparkly unicorns of the sky!

BIG FAT DOOM BUTTON

Which is why I'm creating my own Big Fat Doom Button.

NOT ACTIVA

When I press this button, it'll create a black hole that sucks in unicorns...

And penguins! **Forever!**

No!!!

Evil Master and Keith won't let you get away with this, you mean and horrible cat!

That hurt my feelings, Eugene...

I was about to tell you that you get the pleasure of watching it *all* happen as your friends disappear from existence...

Once and for all!!!

BIG F DOO BUTTO

NOT ACTIVAT

Meanwhile...

This is *ridiculous!* Argh! I can't believe Evil Cat has taken my minion, *again!*

Number 8 – is the Flying Pod of Evil ready?

47

Um, sir. It seems to be gone...

Aaargh! That cat!!!

There is *another*, more environmentally friendly mode of transport...

I hope it's not what I think it is...

Hi, Keith... Eugene's in trouble, do you think you could give sir a lift?

I'm already there!

Well, isn't this just *splendid!*

Okay, so I've connected the stripy wire to the dotty one...

NOT ACTIVATED

It should activate the button, so why is nothing happening?!

I've followed the instructions word for word! Now it's saying something about a purple wire...

There *is* no purple wire!

You're **clearly** not threading the wires correctly. It requires delicate weaving and a few 'cat's cradle' skills. Surely **you** know what 'cat's cradle' is?

Err...

Pfffft! Of **course** I do...

I'll be right back!

Hmm, I have an idea. Now's my chance, while Evil Cat is gone for a moment!

SNAP!

I really hope this works...

Five minutes later...

So, it turns out 'cat's cradle' is *not* a type of 'bed'.

It's a *game* – forming complex patterns with string...

How on earth am I going to do that with all these wires?!

DOOM BUTTON

CTIVATED!

Wait a minute... the Button of Doom has already activated... It wasn't activated before I left!

Well, thank whiskers for that!

Because I had absolutely *no* idea what I was doing...

That also means you *lied* to me, Eugene!

You were just trying to make me sabotage the Big Fat Doom Button!

Well, bad luck, little minion. Let's get this show on the road!

Say goodbye to your unicorn friend in...

50

Three...

BIG F?
DOO?
BTTO?

Two...

DOOM

BASH!

One!!!

Whoa, Keith, what's wrong?

Phew! For a second there, I thought I'd forgotten to defrost tonight's dinner!

That's weird...

ZZZZp

I can't seem to get any closer to Evil Cat's base...

What's that rumbling sound?

51

Gaaaaaaah!!! HOW DOES THIS ALWAYS HAPPEN?!!

Your forcefield might have kept out those sparkly 'unicorns of the sky' you hate so much...

But you never mentioned anything about *unicorns of the sea!*

Are those... narwhals? Well, it seems Eugene has taken care of things himself...

The unicorns of the sea. So beautiful...

SWOOSH

Oh *my...*

Eugene! Why are there **UNICORN** stickers **ALL** over my domination plans?!

Every plan needs a sticker, Evil Master!

Especially a unicorn one!

Heehee, this unicorn looks like a marshmallow!

Please take your marshmallow unicorns **ELSEWHERE!**

Wait. Marshmallows...

And unicorns!

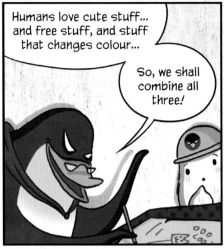

55

Later...

The marshmallow mixture is nearly done, Evil Master!

When the active ingredient turns bright blue, it'll be ready to make into cute little shapes and pack into cute little bags!

We'll need a test subject, hmmm...

The next day...

BONG!

Argh! Who on earth could that be?!

Ooo, post! I never get post!

PLOP

Wow! Free marshmallows?!

FREE CUTE marshmallows

And they change colour when toasted?!

Nobody must know my secret love for things that change colour...

57

KNOCK KNOCK

Argh! Nobody's home!

BURP

BAM

Okay... *you* owe me a new door, and *why* aren't you a marshmallow?!

And *WHY* is there a rainbow coming from your face?

I have too many questions...

I knew there was only *ONE* culprit when I started producing *rainbows.*

So, *where's* the minion?!

EUGENE!!! YOU'RE IN BIG TROUBLE!!! Why is Evil Cat *NOT* a marshmallow?!

Why am I burping *RAINBOWS?!*

60

Number 8, what is this *obscene* TV show?

And why is that guy showing so much of his chest hair?

It's the XTRAORDINARY Factor, sir. A big singing competition.

That man is one of the judges.

Everyone's so emotional... and look, there are thousands of people waiting to be a part of it!

Reality TV is all the rage these days, sir. People love it. Personally, I don't get it.

That's it, Number 8! I shall start my own reality TV show!

Everybody will want to watch my show! They'll be totally *addicted* to it!

64

65

66

An Epple a Day

Eugene! You abominable abomination!

Yes, Evil Master?!

Get your marshmallow face in here this instant!

What's wrong, Evil Master?

Nothing, I just felt like bossing you around.

WAR and GARDEN AS.

What are you eating? Why is it so red and shiny? Are you eating ornaments again?

No, silly! It's an apple from the local farmers' market. It's one of my five a day!

Wait... we have a farmers' market? In the middle of Antarctica?

And what's this about a five a day?!

Well, the humans tell each other to 'eat at least five pieces of fruit or veg each day' to be healthy!

I think they all do it to try to live longer.

69

Let me taste! It'll probably taste like sweaty feet!

Hmmm... it's not bad! I *had* noticed humans are raging about 'healthy eating' and 'superfoods'...

I could use this to my advantage!

Eugene! Fetch me my Evil Notebook of Evil Plans! I have an Evil Plan to note down!

The next day...

My evil invention is working like a dream! It's almost complete, Eugene!

Let me present to you...

10 SECONDS

The Eeple 200™, the next big health craze! And it's a rather attractive shade of blue.

70

Humans will believe an 'Eeple' a day will make them live beyond 200 years old!

But the catch is... an 'Eeple' a day will **SHRINK YOUR** head and thus your **BRAIN!!!**

All thanks to my Evil Gloop.

The humans' brains will shrink so much, they'll become super suggestible, meaning they'll listen to anything I say!

And I will rule the world once and for all!

I need you to inject seven billion apples with Evil Gloop to make them 'Eeples'.

You have *two* days.

Later...

Dooo dooo... I like to eat, eat, eat, eeples and beeneenees!

Are you on target with your batch of Eeples, Neill?

Oh no! You're only meant to inject **one** apple at a time, Neill!

I thought this might save time. You're welcome...

71

The Eeple Machine can't handle more than one at a time! Otherwise it'll—

BOOM!

What was that?! Eugene? Where are you?!

Whoa!!!

Ergh! Why is the Evil Gloop all over the floor?!

ZAP!

Well... why wouldn't it be?!

My hat doesn't fit!

No! It does not fit at all!

Can you help me?

Why, yes! of course!

There you are!

My face!

I'm Neill...

Y'know what? You ARE Neill...

I am! Neill is great!

Sir, I'm back from holiday! How's everyone do—

Oh! Your heads!

Hi, Number 8! Isn't Neill great?!

He is.

I am!

Okay, something's not right...

I'm going to guess that the blue gloopy mess had something to do with this...

Yes, it did!

Neill loaded too many apples and gloop went everywhere.

And Neill is great, so it's okay.

Hmm, we need to get to the bottom of this...

Whoa! What are you doing?!

Getting to the bottom of it!

Not like that, sir!

You'll do anything I say, won't you...

Yes!

Let me try something... I think I should take over the world instead of you. Okay?

I agree! That's fine.

So, you must have been planning to make the humans suggestible...

Well, aren't you going to take over the world then?

Hmm, we need to somehow reverse the effects...

I agree!

Me too!

I think I can make a fruit that enlarges your head and brain...

You definitely can!

Later...

Okay, I've injected some grapes with not-so-evil enlargement gloop...

Each grape contains ten units of not-so-evil gloop, so you only need to eat one to get back to normal...

Ooo yummy!

Whoa...

//POP//

Number 8, you apricot – explain to me what just happened!

Good to have you back, sir!

I'm back too!

Shut up, Neill.

Why won't Eugene's head stop growing?

Oh no! You've eaten the whole bunch of grapes?!

Oh, was I only meant to eat one?

74

75

A PENGUIN'S CHRISTMAS CAROL

It's nearly Chriiiistmas! Oh, Evil Master, isn't it just magical?!

No.

But 'tis the season to be jolly!

BAH BUMHUG!

Heehee... bum.

Look, Evil Master, I have something for you!

It's an early Christmas present.

Whoop-dee-doo.

I think you'll like it, it's very special.

It's a drawing of us in the snow! Do you like it, Evil Master?

love eugenex

If I say yes, will you go away?

Yay! I'm so happy you like it! This is going to be the *best* Christmas ever!

I'll go away now! La la laaaaar!

yawn Off to the Bed of Evil for me.

Enough evil for one day.

SWOOOOOP

78

I am the ghost of your Evil Present.

I despise presents.

No, silly penguin. *The* Present... the *NOW.*

This is all getting a bit technical for me.

Welcome to your Evil Present...

It's Eugene... again.

Oh, I do love a midnight snack!

I probably should've hidden that...

Huh?

CRUNCH

Yoohooooo! Eugene! it was an accident!

He can't hear you.

79

80

Oh my Bob, *no...*

Taking over the world was easier than I thought...

'*Evil Emperor Cat*' just rolls off the tongue, doesn't it?

Yes, oh mighty Evil Emperor Cat.

This can't be happening!

Hey! That's *my* cape!

Minions... Go and dust my 'special' ornament.

Nobody can hear you...

I'm... a *lava statue?* I think I'm going to vomit. This can't be my Evil Future...

All because of a stupid drawing?!

But *is* it just a stupid drawing? It's what it *represents...*

Eugene saw you all as one big family... 'Team Evil Emperor Penguin'!

When you ripped the drawing, Eugene saw this as you tearing his family apart...

Eventually the pain and distress led him back to Evil Cat, who welcomed him and Number 8 with open arms... *as family.*

Seriously... it's just a drawing*!!!*

You must consider the consequences of your actions, Evil Emperor Penguin.

You never know what it could lead to...

Today, I am abolishing spaghetti hoops FOREVER!

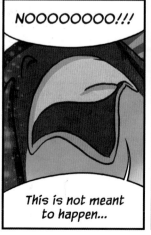

NOOOOOOOO*!!!*

This is not meant to happen...

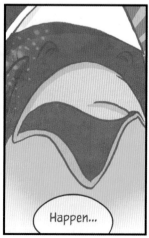

Happen...

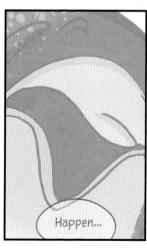

Happen...

82

Evil Master? Are you okay? You kept saying 'happen' over and over...

Look! I made you a drawing of all of us in the snow! Do you like it, Evil Master?

I'm back...

That's very... *team-like*, Eugene. Why don't you put it on the Fridge of Evil...?

Huh?

Just in case I rip it and Evil Cat takes over the world.

Nothing...

Oh, Evil Master, this is going to be the *best Christmas ever!* Let's make spaghetti hoops!

Time to Take Out the Trash

Eugene! Come here, you big armpit hair!

Yes, Evil Master.

I have a new plan I need to explain to you. It's basically a bin.

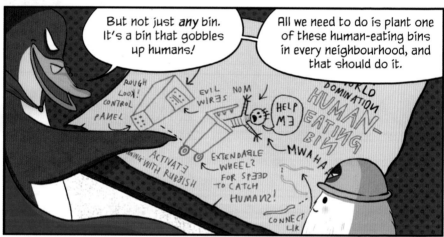

But not just *any* bin. It's a bin that gobbles up humans!

All we need to do is plant one of these human-eating bins in every neighbourhood, and that should do it.

ROUGH LOOK! CONTROL PANEL

EVIL WIRES

NOM

HELP ME

WORLD DOMINATION HUMAN-EATING BIN!

MWAHA

ACTIVATE WITH RUBBISH

EXTENDABLE WHEEL? FOR SPEED TO CATCH HUMANS!

CONNECT LIK

Every human will end up in the trash where they belong, giving me free rein...

To take over the wooooorld!

84

86

87

Neill threw some rubbish in it and it seemed to activate it...

Well, *deactivate* it then...

There is no way to deactivate it. On the upside, the human-eating bin works perfectly!

It's hardly an upside if we're *INSIDE IT!*

Argh! The lid won't open! Isn't there *any* way out of this thing?!

Afraid not. The instructions said to make sure that anyone inside *definitely* couldn't get out...

Look!

A NORMAL BIN

The lid is opening!!! Quick, we can esca–

SPLODGE A NORMAL BIN

Um, sir... what just happened?

Eugene, where did you program the bin to go once it had consumed enough humans?

To the nearest dump, where the rubbish gets squished.

Oh, goody...

Sacré bleu!

The lid is opening again!

That does *not* bode well...

RUBBISH SQUISHER

BOSH!

BUUURP

Well, getting squished was not on today's agenda...

Is it over? are we squished yet?

It didn't hurt as much as I thought...

Huh?

Oh my...

You're doing great, fellow minions! Good job we took that snack break for extra energy!

Yay! We saved Evil Master and Mister 8's life!

RUBBISH SQUISHER

Yay!

Yay!

Oui!

Yay!

Yay!

Yay!

Yay!

Well, since I'm not squished, I'm getting out of this dump....

Sir, what about the minions? We can't—

They'll be fine. Eugene can sort the minons out...

10 hours later...

CREEEAK

RUBBISH SQUISH[ER]

If I let go, I'll be completely squished...

Yay!

Um... yay?

90

FLEGBURT

Eugene, you big potato skin! Get the door!

Of course, Evil Master! Ooo, I wonder who it could be?!

I hope it's the postman with my new unicorn hat!

Oh, hello there.

Greetings! I'm Flegburt!

Oh, hi, Flegburt. I'm Eugene! How can I help you?

Well, I'm a little early actually...

I was sent to destroy your Invention Room of Evil, but I've some spare time before I'm scheduled to do it...

I don't suppose I could pop in for a quick cup of tea?

91

Why, of course! I just boiled the kettle, actually!

Oh, I do appreciate this. I don't want to put you out.

Not at all! I was just counting Evil Master's spaghetti hoop collection.

Well, you are very kind, Eugene! Thank you!

This is Evil Master's Thinking Room of Evil...

I think he's thinking right now!

Um... Evil Master? Flegburt is here to destroy our Invention Room of Evil, but he's a bit early...

I'm going to make him a cup of tea. Is that okay?

Coo-eeee!

I don't care... now, go away! I'm doing Evil Thinking...

Well, he didn't say it *wasn't* okay... so I guess it's okay!

So, what's your story, Flegburt?

I'm Evil Cat's new minion. I started last week. Lovely chap, he is.

Oh, I was Evil Cat's minion once, but I annoyed him too much and I turned into a cloud. *

* See Evil Emperor Penguin: Antics in Antarctica!

92

If Evil Master and Evil Cat are arch-nemeses, does that make us arch-minions?

Or, something arch-y?

I am pondering.

Maybe we're arch-neminions!

Ooo, I like that one!

Here's to arch-neminions!

Oh, I'm terribly sorry, Eugene, but I'm now running late!

I must set everything up and make sure the explosions go off in neat rows of three...

You'd best hurry! Anything else I can do for you, Flegburt?

Oh no, that's okay. I'd best go and destroy your Evil Master's inventions now.

And I should probably warn Evil Master you're going to do it!

Flegburt! Why haven't you blown anything up yet?!

I'm working on it, Evil Master. I don't want to rush anything...

World domination isn't a leisurely walk in the park!

Hurry up! Before that penguin finds you!

Inspired by Eugene, I decorated the *Doom-wire!* It's much prettier now.

Just don't tell me these things...

Stop right there, huge... thing!

Oh, hi! You must be Evil Emperor Penguin! Just give me two seconds!

I just need to intricately thread this Doom-wire into the Circuit Board of Doom...

Please wait... Don't step on that wire... it'll set the Doom Box off too early.

Why am I just standing here watching an overgrown Eugene lookalike set up a *bomb?!*

I do really appreciate your patience... oh, hello again Eugene!

'Hello... *again'?* Eugene, have you met that fluff-mountain already?!

His name is Flegburt! I asked if you'd be okay with him staying for a cup of tea and you didn't say no...

He's Evil Cat's new minion. Isn't he lovely?

What?!

We should probably persuade him not to blow up our evil inventions, though...

Hey, Flegburt? We quite like our inventions, do you think perhaps you could not blow them up?

That's a tad tricky as I have to follow my master's orders.

I respect that... minions must follow their master's orders.

Quite the predicament.

Is this *actually* happening?!

95

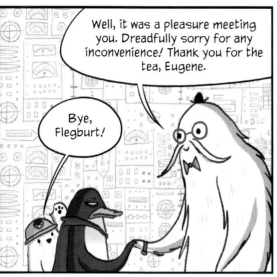

97

THE GREAT CHASE

Evil Master, do you mind if I take a trip to the postbox?

I'm going to post Keith's birthday card!

Eugene, I don't care **what** you do...

...as long as you don't mention the **'K'** word again.

Keith? Or, kipper? Or, katathermometer?

Eugene – be gone!

I hope Keith likes my handmade birthday card!

Shoobee dooo dooo!

Number 8? Where's my Top Secret Envelope of Evil Plans and Passwords?

It's green. I left it right here!

Last time I saw that envelope, it was on your desk, this morning, sir...

BRiiiNG BRiiiNG

Oh, the Evil Phone of Important Phone Calls is ringing for the first time! I should really get it, sir!

Ah-ha! Found it... Wait. What's this?

A birthday card?! *To Keith?* Oh no...

Eugene took the wrong envelope!

Number 8, I have to catch up with Eugene! He's about to post my Top Secret Envelope of Evil Plans and Passwords!

I'll take the Evil-Mobile!

But, sir! Wait! You have a phone call from the Queen for the *first time ever!*

I have to get that envelope before it's too late!

Um, please hold, Mrs Queen!

I'll just get sir...

If you could just hold, Mrs Queen!

Why is Mister 8 in a rush?

Maybe we should be in a rush too?

I agree!

Let's rush, minions! For Mister 8!

Oh, hello! Evil Cat has sent me to destroy you all!

Would that be okay with you?

100

Well, this is fun!

But I just wanted to check that it's okay with you before I destroy you? Or is this a bad time?

Wait... what is my blasted minion doing?!

Flegburt! Come in! What the whiskers are you doing?!

I'm just checking it's okay with the minions first before I destroy them!

OF DOO

Aaaaargh!

Oi, Flegburt! Listen here! Evil villains don't ask permission before destroying their enemies!

Norman, do you feel something?

Digestion?

No. Something feels bad... like Evil-Cat-chasing-Flegburt-and-the-minions-chasing-Number 8-chasing-Evil-Emperor-Penguin-chasing-Eugene bad...

No, I'm not quite getting that. But I am a narwhal.

We must investigate!

104

Number 8! I've successfully hacked into the world leaders' secret Footbook account!

Excellent, sir! Any upcoming world leader events?

I'm not sure yet... I'm only seeing pictures of food and babies in the newsfeed.

Apparently, the Queen of England is with Santa at the cinema watching *Frozen.*

I guess it has royalty and... snow in it?

Wait, did you say... *Santa?*

Ooo, I've found something! A world leaders' bow-tie event on Saturday night, at Big Ben in London!

The perfect opportunity for Evil, sir! What's your plan?

Well, squid, let me tell you!

We are going to give them a bow-tie evening to remember...

POP

I will sneak into the event and by the end of it, I'll be ruler of the world!

But how, sir?

That's for you to work out and me to find out. Now hurry up and come up with something clever so I can take all the credit.

Well, how about something bow-tie related? Maybe a bow tie that blasts some kind of evil laser beam that turns the world leaders into something like... hmmm... like...

Flowers! I bought everyone flowers because I like you!

Number 8, I think I have the answer.

Saturday morning...

Did you pack the Bow Ties of Evil, Eugene?

They're safely tucked inside my unicorn back-pack, Evil Master.

And I packed ten tins of spaghetti hoops in case we get hungry from all the dominating.

Excellent, Eugene! Being *this* evil does make me very hungry.

109

4 hours later...

We've almost reached our destination! Let's make ourselves presentable for our victims!

Are you listening, Eugene? You'd better not be thinking about unicorns again...

My bow tie is your face, Evil Master! Look!

Everything should have my face on it.

And it *shall* when I rule the world!

My bow tie is just your standard bow tie... Or *so you think!*

All I have to do is press the middle of the bow tie and it will release a *purple laser* that will turn whoever it touches into a flower!

Who says world domination can't be pretty?

London...

There's Big Ben, Eugene! And we're right on time!

I feel the urge to stand on the rooftop in a brooding manner.

Do I look brooding?

Hmmm, maybe a little more hip action?

110

How about now?

Hmmm... definitely closer!

...Now?

Maybe more lunging?

Eugene, do you even know what 'brooding' means?

Does it mean 'constipated'?

So how do we get into Big Ben, Evil Master?

That's a valuable question, Eugene...

Pass me my Computer Tablet of Evil!

According to the directions on the Footbook page, it says to 'enter via six o'clock'...

Maybe they mixed up the time with the directions?

No, Eugene. I think the time is the directions...

We have to climb down the clockface...

Isn't that dangerous?

Yes. And that's why you're going first.

What if I fall, Evil Master?

It'll probably hurt... a lot.

Okay... I'm going to step on the big hand...

BONG!

Oh no! I got bonged!

BONG

BONG

Argh! You weigh a tonne, Eugene!

BONG

That'll be all the spaghetti hoops in my backpack.

I'm scared, Evil Master. I'm too cute to die!

Just a little further! Pull yourself up, Eugene!

BONG

Why won't the bongs stop?!

BONG
HEEEAVE!

BEEEP!

Gaaah! Your stupid backpack has activated my Bow Tie of Evil!

Why won't it stop?! I'm pressing the middle... That should deactivate it! And why is it spinning?! Stop! Stop! **Stop!**

Something is wrong with it... It's out of control!

ZZZZZZAAAP!

Evil Master? Are you okay?

Do I *look* okay?!

This is all *your* fault, Eugene!

My unicorn backpack saved me from becoming a lovely flower...

Your backpack is the thing that *caused* this mess!

Oh, and all the spaghetti hoops are now flowers too... oh dear.

But *you* make the most wonderful flower of them all, Evil Master!

I hope I give you hayfever, Eugene.

Back at EEP HQ...

...and then Evil Master was a flower!

Well, that's very rare and unfortunate...

Your *face* is rare and unfortunate.

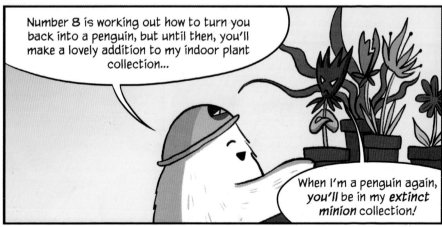

Number 8 is working out how to turn you back into a penguin, but until then, you'll make a lovely addition to my indoor plant collection...

When I'm a penguin again, *you'll* be in my *extinct minion* collection!

EVIL BLOCK

Sir, I'm not so sure firing minions out of a cannon is going to solve anything...

Fine.

BOOM!

Oh... Shooting minions!

Maybe I should make a wish.

Hey, Eugeeeeene!

Hi, Mister 8!

Well, that was a nice surprise!

Hello, Evil Master!

I bought you a month's worth of spaghetti hoops!

They were on special offer... buy one get twenty-nine free!

Evil Master? Are you okay?

Did you forget to put the light on?

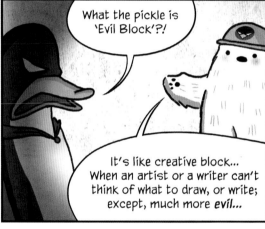

117

Please stop talking, Eugene... It is not relaxing.

That's okay, Evil Master. I know just what to do!

A nice relaxing massage and my special birdsong playlist should do it!

SQUAWK

I taught myself how to massage. I'm pretty much professional level now!

SQUAWK

SQUAWK

Are you relaxed yet?

No... I think you broke my back...

Hmm, let's try some baking instead, then!

Baking is always super fun and relaxing!

It's sure to inspire you!

How about we make an evil flan? It rhymes with 'evil plan'!

BAKING BOOK OF EVIL

4 hours later...

The *Baking Book of Evil* says it's ready when it jiggles...

How about we try some painting?

Paint how you feel... release your emotions...

Hmm...

You **said** paint how I feel...

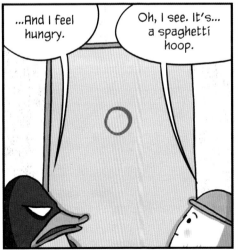

...And I feel hungry.

Oh, I see. It's... a spaghetti hoop.

So do you feel better yet?

Are you inspired to make lots of evil plans?

Whilst the machine massages the human, they will watch a video of me painting a relaxing scene...

Little do they know, they're being *hypnotised!*

After the *hypnotic massage* experience, the human will sit down to a leisurely afternoon tea...

The cakes, once provided, will brainwash the human, once consumed, to believe I am their leader!

And the hypnosis process will be *complete!*

The humans will be wrapped around my little fing– *wing!*

The world will be mine once and for *ALL!*

Isn't that just the best idea, Eugene? Aren't I a *genius?!*

Eugene?

Eugene, you pathetic garden gnome, where are you?

Oh, hi, Evil Master...
You seem to have launched me from your cannon all the way to Peru. I'm on my way back though. Only 5,340 miles to go.

Where have you been, idiots?! My latest evil plan for world domination is ready and waiting!

You shot us out of a cannon, sir...

That's no excuse, squid!

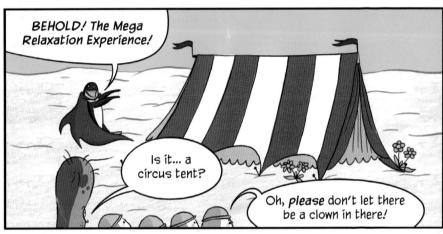

BEHOLD! The Mega Relaxation Experience!

Is it... a circus tent?

Oh, *please* don't let there be a clown in there!

No... it is not a circus tent, Number 8. How dare you.

Oh... it's just... never mind.

I've sent out special invitations to all the world leaders...

They will receive a free trial of the Mega Relaxation Experience.

Comes with a free cape... No world leader can resist a cape! Everyone knows a cape makes you *one thousand* times more awesome.

122

Ooo, my first RSVP!

INVITATION TO MEGA
RELAXATION EXPERIENCE
— ACCEPTED —
BY HM QUEEN
OF ENGLAND!

From the Queen of England! My evil plan is working!

Next day...

Number 8, have you set up the hypnotic painting video? And arranged the Towels of Evil? In order of fluffiness?

Yes, yes, and *of course*, sir.

Eugene! Have you baked all the Cakes of Evil for the post-massage afternoon tea? Remember to add Essence of Evil to the teapot!

Of course, Evil Master!

And don't forget the Cherry of Evil on top of the Sponge of Evil!

My Evil Plan is coming together wonderfully!

DING DONG!

And the Queen has arrived just in time!

I brought my corgis along, I hope you don't mind?

Your corgis ride penny-farthings?

...Never mind. Do follow me along the red carpet to your Mega Relaxation Experience.

Right through here, ma'am, Queen of Englandshire.

Golly... is that a circus tent?

Ugh... stay calm and collected... you will rule her soon enough...

123

124

I travelled all this way and you're not even going to offer me a massage?

Take the free cape and leave.

I don't want the cape.

What do you want, then?

World domination, of course... But it's a little hard when *you* also want the same thing. So, what I *really* want, Evil Emperor Penguin...

Is to eliminate my competition!

That's *you,* by the way, in case you were wondering...

If nobody's going to have a massage, I might try it out if that's dandy?

Go *away,* Flegburt.

Well, this is nice.

Ooo, there's a video of Evil Emperor Penguin painting a picture. How lovely!

Evil Cat, you're wasting my time. Go and lick your behind.

Oh, I *will*... but at least let me shrink you first!

126

Meanwhile...

I best go check to see if Evil Master needs any help with hypnotising the Queen...

Ooo, what's that on the ground?

A large curly whisker? *Gasp!*

I only know one creature who'd have a whisker as curly as that...

Evil Cat!

What's going on in here? Where's the Queen and Evil Master?

Not until you tell me where Evil Master is!

Oh, Eugene! If you could just give me that whisker...

Well, that's a good question...

Why are you on the floor?

Just give me the whisker and I'll tell you!

128

Wait... is that why you want your whisker back? You can't stand up without it!

I have power over you! Yay!

I'd forgotten how annoying you are...

You help me find Evil Master and I'll give you your whisker back.

I can't believe I'm bargaining with the minion of my arch-nemesis. *Fine!*

Now... where did you put Evil Master?

I shrank him... He stole my whisker and ran off... Then, well, this.

I found the whisker by the drain. He must've fallen in!

And what do you propose we do now?!

I can't believe you shrank us using *my* shrink ray and then pushed me down the drain!

SPLOSH

131

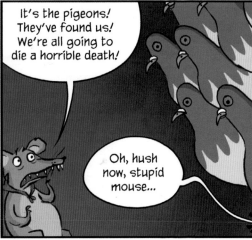

134

135

What makes you so sure?

Because it says so on that massive screen over there...

P.I.A.
PIGEON INTELLIGENCE AGENCY
ALWAYS ● WATCHING

Oh.

What on earth does the P.I.A. do?

I think they strive to protect the world from supervillains, stopping them from carrying out their dodgy deeds...

Pah! That can't be right! A group of silent pigeons capturing supervillains?!

Well, it says so right there...

ING

STRIVING TO PROTECT THE WORLD FROM THE MOST DASTARDLY VILLAINS – STOPPING THEM FROM CARRYING OUT THEIR DODGY DEEDS...

Do they have a screen for everything?

RDLY VILLAINS – CARRYING OUT EEDS...

YES

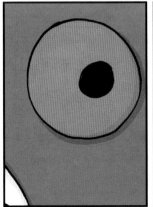

So that's it, we're stuck in this pigeon cage forever now?

We're three supervillains and a cute minion! Surely we can come up with something?!

You're right, Evil Master!

Two hours later...

I've got nothing...

Can you believe this all stemmed from you having Evil Block, Evil Master?

Can you believe in **shutting right up**, Eugene?!

Mint, anyone?

Do you hear something?

Sorry, that's probably my rumbling tummy.

No... Something more old-fashioned.

139

Like the wheels of a penny-farthing? That can mean only *one* thing!

Flegburt!

How could your minion *possibly* know where we are?

Never underestimate Flegburt...

We've been shrunk to the size of rats and locked up by pigeon spies...

Evilness knows where we are in the world!

Ooo! I'm gonna guess... Spain?

And we're stuck in here with this rat who won't shut up...

Is it Spain, though?

You'll all be sorry when I am saved and you're left here to get eaten by those creepy pigeons!

CREEEEEAAAAK

Oh no! The pigeons have come to gobble us up!

There you are! Inside the bark of a Pinus Pinaster tree no less! How quaint!

Flegburt!

I told them it was you! But they didn't believe me!

Now, take me home. I can't walk... I'm missing my–

...Whisker?

I found it floating in the river Douro...

That's a Spanish river! I *was* right... We're in Spain!

In your face!

Here's your whisker. Oh, and your hat...

I found your hat too, Eugene!

Thanks, Flegburt! You're my favourite enemy!

What about his cape?

I don't have a cape...

But all supervillains have a cape! Look... You're the only one here without one. You may as well be a minion.

You should've taken that free one I offered you...

Well, I might be the only one without a cape, but I'm also the only one who's escaping this place!

I hope your capes keep you warm! C'mon Flegburt, let's go!

Oh no, we can't leave without Evil Emperor Penguin - the one and only ruler of the world!

Um, what?

Yeah, what?

After a nice massage, an inspiring video and a cup of tea, I couldn't stop thinking about you! I simply had to find you!

Wait a minute...

You were using my Mega Relaxation Experience! It really works!

Flegburt... *who is your world leader?*

Why, *you* are, of course, Evil Emperor Penguin!

You're wrong! I, Evil Cat, am your leader!

...The evil invention **actually works!**

Hundreds of world leaders were queueing up to have a massage in your circus tent after me!

gasp Really?!

Oh, yes...

But I told them to go home because you weren't there... And I had to find you first.

What?! Please tell me you're joking?!

Of course not. I would never joke to you, oh Evil One, ruler of the world!

I can't believe I could have had all the world leaders under my control... And instead I end up with *Flegburt* under my control!

I... I have no words.

Ha! Just like the pigeons! Use one of their big screens to express your emotions...

I'll express *your* emotions with my fist if you don't shut up!

I'm so glad I used my finest tracking skills to find you, Evil Emperor Penguin!

I am forever yours to boss around...

No, Flegburt! *I* am your Evil Master! You are *my* minion! Stop this nonsense!

No, Mr Cat, Evil Emperor Penguin is my Evil Master!

I did not see this coming...

Um, guys. I literally have no idea what's going on, but we should probably get out of here before the pigeons realise what's happening!

C'mon then, there's enough room here for all of you on my arm!

Do you ever get the feeling you're being watched?

Flegburt! You'd better run! Get us out of here!

I have this under control...

How? There are *thousands* of those silent, deadly pigeons!

144

Well. This is the part where we all die.

Well, sweet whiskers of mine, we've had some good times...

No yays!

Tell my wife I love her!

Wait... I hear pecking, but it's not our faces being pecked to death...

Luckily I had a spare sandwich packed...

Everyone knows a pigeon can't resist a nice breadcrumb.

They should stay distracted for exactly eight minutes, that's enough time to escape!

All aboard the penny-farthing!

I have to admit, Flegburt. You're not bad.

Maybe I will keep you to boss around.

Yay! I love Flegburt!

Flegburt! Don't listen to him! *You've been hypnotised!*

Flegburt...

Yes, Evil Master Penguin, sir?

Dispose of Evil Cat. And the weird rat.

145

146

PLAN POOVER

Number 8. Go and remove that massive rainbow from outside. It's distracting me.

Um, sir, I don't have the ability to do that.

DING-DONG!

Number 8, go and get the door! Or do you *'not have the ability'?!*

Oh, erm, hello... How can I help you?

Errr...

Howdy! You must be Number 8! I'm Colin!

I'm here for my work experience with Evil Emperor Penguin!

It's part of my Sparkle Scouts Career Badge.

My uncle Keith said you wouldn't mind... I'm so excited!

Clearly, Keith doesn't know sir at all...

Erm, sir...

I have a Colin here to do work experience with you.

Number 8, when are you going to learn to stop speaking in tongues?

147

It's an honour to meet you, Mr Evil, sir!

Uncle Keith tells me so much about you!

You look like one of Eugene's drawings...

Number 8, please escort the Christmas decoration out. I have important Evil things to focus on.

I can help!

I'm afraid Colin is in our care for now, sir. Keith put your name down as Colin's work experience placement.

RAINBOW RANGERS

SEAL OF APPROVAL

It's all official with the unicorn 'Seal of Approval' 'n' everything...

Evil Master, I finished the calculat—

TINY FLUFFY UNICORN!!!

You must be the cute minion...

EUGEEEEEENE!

YAY! YAY! YAY!

TWITCH

Next day...

Argh! Why can't I think of a good domination plan?! And I can't focus with your fluorescent pink mane all up in my peripherals! Look at this *mess!*

Hey! Put down my Crayons of Evil right now!

And why are you drawing with your right *and* left?! Stop this witchcraft this instant!

You mentioned mess and it made me think about cleaning up and then I thought...

Super Epic Human Rainbow Vacuum!!!

Otherwise known as 'Plan Poover'. Allow me to explain...

The fuel for the Poover could be unicorn poo! It's two thousand times more powerful than nuclear energy.

And much better for the environment!

The Poover fan will keep the unicorn poo churning and the humans moving in a constant flow.

Before we Poover up the humans, we can pump out a sufficent amount of the purply bit of the rainbow through the Poover exhausts.

The purply bit contains properties that have calming effects...

That way, the humans will enter a dream-like state...

POWER PACK

And thus, be much easier to catch.

I just remembered the Toilet of Evil needs a deep clean...

Go and show Colin where the cleaning products are kept.

But...

Now!

Cleaning the Toilet of Evil isn't that bad...

You can make it fun by singing while you scrub!

Later...

Hmmm...

HOW TO DEAL WITH UNUSUALLY INTELLIGENT UNICORNS

BANG!

151

But, sir, what are you doing? The Poover worked!

Number 8... a unicorn just conquered the world! It's *my* job to take over the world!

AND I MUST GET ALL THE CREDIT!!!

Okay, Poover. It's just you and me. Now we shall get all the praise for taking over the world. The way it was *meant* to be!

I'll show that sparkle-horse who does the world dominating around here!

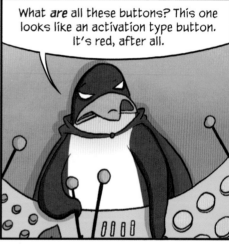

What *are* all these buttons? This one looks like an activation type button. It's red, after all.

Hmm, that didn't work. Maybe *this* button. And *this* lever.

Nothing...

Do *any* of these buttons work?!

Work! You stupid—

BASH!! BASH! BASH!

EVIL PRINTER

Sir, a package arrived for you.

Ooo, is it full of world domination, Number 8?

Um, I'm not sure world domination comes in the post, sir...

Then I'm not interested.

It's cube-shaped, if that helps?

Yay, Evil Master has a mystery cube!

This is so exciting!

Well, I guess we should open it...

According to the instruction manual it's an 'Evil Printer', sent by Mr Lukas Butler.

What am I meant to do with it?!

This is some genius stuff right here...

So it's a device that is disguised as a printer, but it produces Evil Paper! This is amazing!

And when you write on the Evil Paper, the writing appears on this Evil Screen!

We could distribute the Evil Paper to all of the world leaders so when they write on it, all of their secrets will be revealed to me, right here!

But first, I have a delightfully Evil Plan to finally foil that wretched arch-nemesis of mine!

Go away!

DING DONG

DELIVERY!

PLOP

'To Evil Cat, congratulations on winning this notebook.'

Well, isn't that just marvellous! I've never won anything before!

Later that night...

Hmmm...

PING!

The lightbulb is flashing! Evil Cat must be writing on the Evil Paper!

155

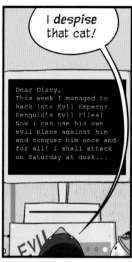

I *despise* that cat!

Dear Diary,
This week I managed to hack into Evil Emperor Penguin's Evil Files! Now I can use his own evil plans against him and conquer him once and for all! I shall attack on Saturday at dusk...

Thank goodness for the Evil Paper!

Otherwise we'd never have known Evil Cat's plans!

Saturday...

Mwahahaaar!

With my super-silent turbo engine, that penguin will never know I'm here!

What the...?! He can't have possibly known I was here!

Hey! Those purple things are ruining my Whiskers 5000!

SPLODGE
SPLODGE
SPLODGE
SPLODGE

Argh! They're sticking like glue!

Oi! It's chipping the paintwork!

We got him, Number 8! The purple snot-balls are working a treat! Good work, minions!

Y'know, I always forget that I have 249 *other* minions hanging around the place.

SCRIBBLE SCRIBBLE

Well, Diary,
One stupid point to the stupid penguin. I'm so angry right now, I can't even wear my hat. HE WILL PAY!!! Tomorrow, I'm using 'The Cake Ray'...

156

The next day...

Right on time...

Prepare to be baked, Evil Emperor Penguin!

CREEEAK

ZZZZFFFMMM

CAKE RAY

Activate!

Please tell me you didn't just sacrifice ten of your minions?!

Eleven, actually...

Oh, come on, as long Eugene is fine, that's all that matters, right?!

I'm okay!

Dear Diary,
I don't understand...
Evil Emperor Penguin
was ready for me
again! THIS time I'll
foil that caped beast!
He'll never be able to
beat my robotic tiger!

EVIL

PING

Activate! C'mon! Activate!

I'm pressing the red button, why aren't the laser eyes working?!

Why won't you work?!

What's that familiar noise?

Not again!!!

Nice work on swapping the red buttons, Eugene!

Keith would be proud!

Well, Diary, I'm not sure how, but that penguin always seems to be one step ahead of the game. THIS IS ABSURD!

MUNCH MUNCH MUNCH

I was going to hynotise him with my hypnotic violin, but he replaced the violin with a viola, and I can't tell the difference.
It turns out I can't play the viola.

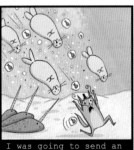

I was going to send an army of narwhals to attack Evil Emperor Penguin, but he already had seal missiles waiting for me. There were also fishy ice bombs...
One hit my bum.

OM NOM NOM

I was going to train a bunch of sharks to bite bums, but Evil Emperor Penguin had ALREADY trained them to eat anything with a curly moustache (except Number 8). Stupid octopus.

The only place I've been writing my secret plans is in this notebook---

Wait a minute...

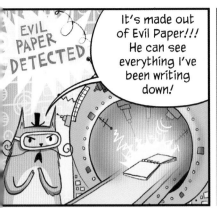

159

160

It's raining spaghetti hoops!

It's beautiful.

I'd forgotten last time I visited the spaghetti hoop factory, they gave out loads of 'delete' stickers. I stuck them everywhere because it was super fun!

Why would they give you dele— Y'know what, never mind.

Back at EEP HQ...

Sir, the Evil Printer seems to have run out of Evil Paper...

Gah! We wasted it all on that ridiculous cat! Was worth it, though...

The other functions still work!

PANCAKES INITIATED

PING

Let's have pancakes!

FLEGBURT'S TRUE CALLING

Number 8! Where have all my capes gone?!

There should be at least five clean capes in your Wardrobe of Evil, sir.

Well, they must be *so* clean that I can't see them!

I can't *possibly* take over the world without an Evil Cape!

I saw Flegburt with a pile of them earlier, sir. He said he was going to wash them for you.

Argh, that minion is more trouble than he's worth! Last week he ironed my Evil Diary, and yesterday he tried to bake a cake and ended up baking Neill.

Evil Master! I'm in a bit of a pickle... I tried to wash your capes, but I accidentally put them in the blender instead.

Flegburt... you need to get out before I do something Number 8 will regret.

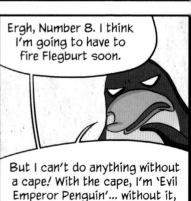

Ergh, Number 8. I think I'm going to have to fire Flegburt soon.

But I can't do anything without a cape! With the cape, I'm 'Evil Emperor Penguin'... without it, I'm just 'Evil Emperor Penguin Without a Cape'.

163

Wow...

It's like there's every cape imaginable in here...

I wonder if they sell Dishwasher Tablets of Evil... I think I accidentally ate the last batch.

Let's shop!

CAPES

MINION HATS

MONOCLES

FLAGS

COLLARS ARE THE NEW BAD

Time to try these on!

Why are you looking for a new cape anyway, eh?

Don't you have, like, fifteen of the same one?

Flegburt blended them all up.

Oh, you mean, *my* minion who *you* brainwashed and stole from me...

Seriously, you can have him back.

Maybe I don't want him back... I've got Evil Rat now!

Hi!

But, Evil Master, can't we keep Flegburt?

No...

Eugene... *what* are you *wearing?!*

Oh, I think perhaps I wasn't meant to hear any of that...

166

How bad do you guys feel right now?!

Shut up, Evil Rat, or else I'll eat you.

I'd bought you a shower cap, Evil Master Penguin, sir, to say sorry for blending up your capes.

And ruining your diary and eating your dishwasher tablets...

Ergh, Flegburt. It's just not working out.

It's okay. I understand. I'm not entirely sure I was meant to be a minion, anyway. I always wanted to be an accountant.

I think you'll make a lovely accountant, Flegburt.

Ooo, where did that gust of wind come from?

It's making all this lovely cape wrap itself around me.

Gasp! Flegburt...

Have you ever considered a cape before? You'd look brilliant as a superhero!

167

That's it, loveliest minion Eugene!

My true calling!

He looks really good in a cape...

Too good.

He looks better than I ever could... This is *not fair!*

That's true, you don't suit capes, Evil Cat.

I will make sure taxes are paid on time, and that businesses run efficiently!

I will strive to be the superhero the world needs!

Say hello to your shiny new superhero accountant!

I don't understand what's happening right now?

Flegburt is moving on to bigger, better, more mathematical things...

Thank you for everything you've done for me, Evil Villains.

And Eugene, you'll always be my best minion friend.

I loved working with both you, Evil Cat, and you, Evil Emperor Penguin.

I just found the best selection of monocles... Oh, what just happened?

Is that... Flegburt... flying away?

Flegburt just left us to become a superhero accountant.

Do you think he's going to pay for that cape?

A week later...

Flegburt's on TV!

Are you in need of heroic financial advice? Well, you know who to call!

CAPTAIN ACCOUNTANT!

At the end of the tax year, there's NO NEED to fear, for Captain Accountant will ALWAYS be here!

Now Flegburt is a 'superhero', doesn't that technically make him our enemy?

I guess it does! And what a lovely enemy he will be.

Excellent.

Now go and return that stupid hat to the shop, Eugene. It is not becoming.

SHAMPOOGENE

Number 8, I have a plan!

An *evil* plan, sir?

So *incredibly* evil, you'll eat your monocle!

Oh, I say! And what is it?

SHAMPOO!

Oh, that sounds so... *evil*, sir. And what do you intend to do with *shampoo?*

Allow me to explain!

I plan to create a Super Shampoo of Evil that will give you your *dream* hair-do!

There will be a shampoo that makes your hair curly or straight or long or purple if you wish. There's a shampoo for everyone!

But here's the catch...

The more you wash your hair with my Super Shampoo of Evil, the more you'll be brainwashed to think *I* am your *master!*

Thanks to the addition of my Secret Essence of Brainwash.

To every bottle of Super Shampoo of Evil, a spoonful of Essence of Brainwash will be added...

It'll smell like hope and world domination...

And roses.

Soon, the humans will bow down to *me!*

And have super shiny hair!

Excellent plan, sir! Simple *and* effective!

It *is* simple and effective! Just like *you*, Number 8.

Eugene! Get to work on my Evil Plan right now!

Oh, I was just about to have a cookie break, Evil Master.

No cookies! It's all about me and world domination now.

You'll be making the Super Shampoo of Evil. I've provided the Evil bit – Essence of Brainwash. You add all the nice bits like flower smells and all that rubbish.

I'm good at nice rubbish.

Later...

LONG READY

NOT CURLY READY

NOT SPIKY READY

NOT PATCHY READY

ESSENCE OF BRAINWASH

PING!

Yay! The first bottle of Long Hair Evil Shampoo is ready!

Only three billion one hundred and eighty million, six hundred thousand two hundred and ninety nine bottles to go! Then on to the next set...

Time to add some nice ingredients to make it smell less Evil.

Maybe I'll add some daisy juice... and some strawberry seeds!

Ooo, and some unicorn tears for sparkle.

What's 'Essence of Hydra'? Must be for extra *hydration!* I'll add that too!

This is going to be the most wonderful Evil Shampoo in the world!

Maybe I'll just try a little bit...

I already know Evil Master is my Evil Master, so all it'll do is make me smell lovely!

172

Ooo, it seems to be frothing up rather a lot.

Hmmm that's better. And I smell great!

Next morning...

Eugene! It's 5am! Why aren't you up and working on the Evil Shampoo?!

I'm in a bit of a situation, Evil Master.

I'll give you a situation in a minute!

Oh...

Okay, we have a situation...

Well, I think my hair grew a bit overnight. I tried to cut it, but it's growing too fast...

Is there any point in asking you how this happened?

I was testing the long hair batch...

It appears to work quite well.

'Quite well'?! It appears to still be growing!

And now it's wrapping around my leg! Stop that, Eugene!

I'm not doing anything, Evil Master. Maybe my hair really likes you?

Number 8! Get in here now! Eugene's hair is invading my personal space!

And it smells like heavenly flowers...

Don't just stand there, squid! *Help!*

Maybe I could try cutting it?

I already tried that, Mister 8. it's growing too fast.

I have eight tentacles so I can cut it eight times as fast. That might help...

Oh *my*... it's not just growing, it's *multiplying* every time I cut it!

What on earth did you add to the Evil Shampoo, Eugene?!

Umm, a few drops of daisy juice, some unicorn tears, strawberry seeds. Oh, and some Essence of Hydra.

Essence of Hydra?!

I figured it would be good to add for hydrating your hair.

No, you wombat! Extract of Hydra does *not* hydrate!

For every strand chopped off, it'll multiply into *more!* Like the hydra serpentine water monster myth!

I was going to use it for *another* Evil Plan!

It won't stop growing!

How do you destroy hydras then, Evil Master?

With fire...

Oh...

This is *ridiculous!*

Evil Cat's HQ

BING BONG

Hmmm, my moustache curler is early today.

Evil Rat! Get the door, will you?!

Um... we have a problem. Things have got a bit *hairy* around here...

Well, deal with it, then. I'm busy updating my Footbook status.

THE UNPOPPABLE PLAN

Evil Master, look what I've got...

I don't care, Eugene.

But look! Bubbles!

I got them for free at Keith and Norman's wedding.

Ergh! Begone, small transparent spheres of doom!

Wait a minute! That's given me a perfectly well-rounded world domination idea!

I'll make a bubble machine that will create the biggest unpoppable bubbles you've ever seen!

Hee hee, only *you* could make bubbles evil, Evil Master!

On contact, the bubble will consume you and you'll be trapped inside an unpoppable bubble forever.

That doesn't sound too evil...

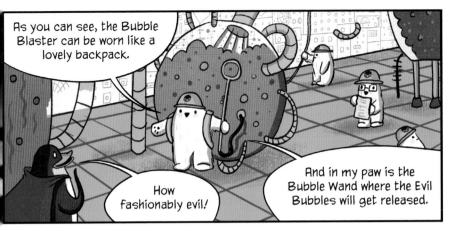

As you can see, the Bubble Blaster can be worn like a lovely backpack.

How fashionably evil!

And in my paw is the Bubble Wand where the Evil Bubbles will get released.

You can activate the bubbles by pressing the red button on the Bubble Wand handle.

And the green button plays Evil Music...

It's important that you have an Evil Theme Tune whilst you Bubble Blast world leaders!

Look, I'll play it for you!

BEEP!

'I'm forever blooowing buuuubbllllles!'

Eugene...

180

181

182

Do you guys need a ride back?

If we hurry, we might still catch the world leaders' meeting!

Let's just take a minute for a group selfie!

Totally making this my new Unigram profile picture!

Weeeeeeeee! Almost there, grumpy penguin!

Number 8! I'm back! Prepare the Bubble Blaster!

Let the Bubblegeddon *commence!*

Oh, I'm afraid you just missed the world leaders... if you'd been one minute earlier, you would've caught them.

That selfie has ruined everything!

Already got one 'like' from Eugene on Unigram, though!

A Christmas to Remember

Evil Master, do you want socks for Christmas this year?

No, Eugene. Every year you ask me and every year I say *no*...

I want only one thing... *world domination!*

I hope I'm on Santa's Nice List.

I think I've been extra good this year!

Well, I've been extra naughty, so I'm hoping for a nice batch of coal... Free fuel for my Speedboat of Evil.

Argh! There's nothing but Christmas films on television. Not even *one* documentary about spaghetti hoops!

Christmas films make me feel warm and fuzzy.

Sir, your Post Interceptor of Evil appears to be jammed. Since it's only a week until Christmas, it's intercepted everybody's letters to Santa.

Has it detected anything of importance amongst the pathetic Santa letters?

Christmas...

I'm not sure, sir. Since it's jammed, the scanner has shut down.

We may have to sort through the post manually, I'm afraid.

Well, get the minions to do it, then.

But, sir, there are over one million letters to sort through...

Then they'd better get to work *quickly.*

Yay! I love sorting!

It's a good job, Eugene, because you've a lot to get through!

Okay, fellow minions, let's sort!

Is it break time yet?

We've only just started, Gary!

186

Two days later...

Aww look, it's the Queen of England's Christmas list.

She'd really like a crown with flashing lights on it.

Ooo, I found Evil Cat's rejection from 'The Great British Bake Off'.

Y'know what I think, Neill? I think Santa is magic... Like the wizard of Christmas or something.

I guess?

Eugene... I want to hear less talking and more envelope opening!

But, Evil Master, don't *you* think that Santa *must* be magic?

You are far too obsessed with that bearded gnome.

But, Evil Master... Santa visits *every* single house in the world, in just *one* night!

And he remembers what present belongs to *each* person in *every* house... he *must* be magic!

And he must be a really nice guy if everyone's willing to let him into their house without even a key.

See?! Santa is amazing!

187

DING!

Oh, Evil Master, there's a lightbulb above your head... shall I turn it off for you?

Eugene, I have just had *the* ultimate world domination idea!

Who's the one guy who has access to everyone's address and doesn't need permission to enter their home once a year?!

Santa!

And who will be delivering presents to all the world leaders this Christmas Eve?

Santa!

No, Eugene... that is where you are wrong!

Because Santa will be taking a little break this year...

Oh no, is he okay?

He'll be just fine, when he eats my sleep-inducing mince pies and I lock him up.

But Santa needs to be awake for Christmas!

Eugene... *I will* be awake. *I will* take Santa's place.

Oh, well, that's very kind of you to help out whilst he's sleeping and locked up.

On Christmas Eve I will gain access to all the homes of all the humans of the world, including the *world leaders!*

Nobody will bat an eyelid if I'm dressed as Santa. I will *easily* be able to capture *whomever I want!*

I can't believe I've never thought of this before, Eugene! I am a genius!

A Christmas genius!

So, can we call you Santa yet?

No, Eugene... Don't *ever* call me that.

Also, go and shave... You look like a walking beard.

Later...

Santa doesn't live too far away... Look!

Wrong pole, Eugene...

So, what's the plan of action, sir?

189

Once I've dealt with Santa, I'll find his 'World Address Book' and take the reins... *Literally!*

I shall make my way to each world leader's home, and using my *Gift-zapper 3000*, they'll get wrapped up in some **very** pretty paper...

Once every world leader is gift-wrapped, I'll fly them to the Moon...

But that's not all...

I'll then erase their memories, so they have no idea what happened!

Disguising myself as Santa is my best move yet! The world will be *mine!*

This could actually work!

All I ever wanted for Christmas was to take over the world...

And this year, it's about time I got what I wanted! Mwahahahaaaar!

Oh, I was always under the impression you wanted some new socks...

No, Eugene. I have already told you – *I don't want* socks! I don't even *wear* socks!

Okay, Number 8, prepare the sleep-inducing mince pies for Santa and fetch my *Memory Eraser* device!

Yes, sir!

190

Eugene... you and the other minions have until Christmas Eve to build my Gift-zapper 3000. Here's the blueprint...

GIFTZAPPER 3000

Test it on that minion with the glasses. He won't mind. Oh, and then shave him to make my Santa beard...

Christmas Eve morning

Hey, Neill!

Hey, Eugene! What have you got there?

Am I being... *Gift-wrapped?!*

GIFTZAP!

Maaaaybe...

Well, that works just fine... Thanks, Neill!

That's... Okay?

Now, I just need to unwrap you and then shave off your fur...

Okay... it's time!

Good luck, sir. I'll be in touch with you the whole way, in case you need any help.

You make the best Evil Santa ever! The beard suits you too...

191

Ho ho ho, I'm very busy preparing for tonight, so this will need to be qui—

Hello -lo-lo?

Ooo! Ho ho ho! a mince pie pie pie!

Well, what d'ya know know know! There's another one!

Yum yum yum! These are tasty!

Ooo, Santa's Naughty and Nice List...

How is Evil Cat on the Nice List?! Let's change that right now!

Gasp There it is! Santa's address book...

Every address imaginable is in here... even the Tooth Fairy's.

Which reminds me, she owes me at least five pounds.

Hmmm, what else can I steal from Santa's house before I go kidnap all the world leaders and take over the world?

Oh yes... a sleigh, of course!

I'm here to ruin your life, as usual...

Don't you know the drill by now, Evil Emperor Penguin?

You try to take over the world, and I get in the way... You fail... I'm happy. You're grumpy. And then we do it all again.

Thing is, you're actually on to something this time. I must say, your Christmas plan is a good one. And that's not me humouring you...

So as you can imagine, I feel a bit upset. Once you take over the world, who will I torment?

You'll be *far* too busy to play with.

And since I sacked my co-villain, Evil Rat, I'm going to be *very* bored. And I can't have that...

You're boring *me* now, Evil Cat... Go *away!*

How *rude*... You never *did* learn any manners *did you?!*

Go away, *please?!*

I don't have time for this. I'm off to take over the world and you're *too late* to stop me!

Fair enough... off you pop.

Oh, but there *is* one thing I should probably mention...

Aaaargh! What?!

I have some of your friends here...

The unicorn was a bonus!

He's going to take our memories!

Okay, you just ruined my big Evil Reveal! Who even is that?

No idea...

It's me, Neill! *NEILL!*

Anyway, as I was saying...

Using my state-of-the-art wireless technology, I've synced your Memory Eraser with my very own Memory-Wiper right here...

As soon as you activate *your* Memory Eraser on the world leaders, it'll activate this one *here*... on your friends!

What?! No!

What do you care?!

You'll have the *world!* Evil Emperor Penguin doesn't need friends to rule the world... *does he?*

Later...

So, there's this cat who is my arch-nemesis, and he is always foiling my Evil Plans...

He's now holding Number 8, Eugene, Keith and that-one-with-the-glasses hostage. And if I take over the world, they'll never remember ever knowing me...

All the memories gone... just like that.

I mean, world domination is all I've ever wanted! And this is my chance to finally have it!

What should I *do?* What would *you* do, Dasher?!

Look, mate, my degree is in sleigh-pulling, not mentoring villains.

I can't let anyone get in my way! *I'm doing this!*

C'mon, Rudolph, guide us to our first stop...

...The Queen of England!

GIFTZAP!

Remember the time Evil Master got chased by a hunky virus inside a computer?!

Haha! That was a good one... and when you and sir got turned into babies!

GIFTZAP!

GIFTZAP!

I remember when Evil Master went loopy because his spaghetti hoops got stolen!

GIFTZAP! GIFTZAP! GIFTZAP! GIFTZAP! GIFTZAP! GIFTZAP! GIFTZAP! GIFTZAP! GIFTZAP! GIFTZAP! GIFTZAP! GIFTZAP! GIFTZAP! GIFTZAP!

Any moment now! Heeeheeeee!

Three hours later...

What's taking him so long?!

Surely he'd be on the Moon by now!

Yes, well, things... change.

I can't have you forgetting who's boss, can I?!

I'm sure the world leaders won't mind spending this Christmas on the Moon.

I left a note for Santa telling him to go and collect them tomorrow. He owes me.

Yay, Evil Master! *You love us!*

Don't use the 'L' word, Eugene! It's offensive.

What do we do with Evil Cat now?

Well, he's had his memory erased, so I guess he's not your arch-nemesis any more...

Christmas night...

Mr Penguin, remind me how long I've been your minion for?

Not long enough. And that's *Evil Master* to you.

Squid, tell Neill to shut up.

This is the best Christmas ever! And I bought you *all* socks!

Of course, sir.

Evil Master remembered who I am!

207

THE END!

HOW TO DRAW EEP!

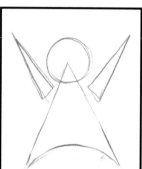

Using a pencil, lightly draw a small circle and a triangle with a curved bottom (hehe). This will be the template for EEP's body...

Again, using your pencil lightly add EEP's arms (like he is manically laughing!) then draw his feet.

Now you can use a darker pencil or a pen to draw EEP's body outline leaving a gap for his manic laugh.

Next, add EEP's triangular eye and his beak! Then add a light curve on his belly. You can erase the rough pencil lines if you wish.

Now for the important part... The CAPE! And don't forget to colour the cape in bright red!

Add the rest of the colour. Start with the grey body. yellow beak and feet. Leave a white patch on his belly, but add a very light yellow shade at the top. TAH-DAH!

THE PHOENIX

GREAT STORIES EVERY WEEK

This special preview of *The Phoenix* will give you a glimpse of some of the **AMAZING** stuff inside every issue, including brand-new comics by artists like Jamie Smart, **EVERY WEEK!**

TURN THE PAGE to read more and see what else is in *The Phoenix*!

SPECIAL PREVIEW!

The Phoenix is the only place you can read the NEWEST Megalomaniacs!

THE PHOENIX

GREAT STORIES EVERY WEEK

THE SKILLS HUB

DRAW YOUR MONSTERS

With Zak Simmonds-Hurn

WE'RE LEARNING HOW TO DRAW MONSTER PARTS, SO WE CAN BUILD OUR OWN MONSTER!

EYES, TEETH AND FANGS

MONSTROUS EYEBALLS

LET'S MAKE THOSE PEEPERS INTO CREEPERS!

JUST START WITH CIRCLES! ONE FOR THE EYEBALL, ONE FOR THE IRIS, ONE FOR THE PUPIL, LIKE THIS.

TO ADD SOME SHINE, LEAVE A SMALL WHITE CIRCLE IN THE PUPIL AND A CURVED RECTANGLE OVERLAPPING PART OF THE IRIS.

TO MAKE AN EYE-BALL LOOK VEINY, DRAW THIN, WIGGLY, BRANCHING LINES AROUND THE EDGE OF THE EYE.

YOU COULD PUT YOUR EYES ON STALKS FOR A REALLY STRANGE LOOK! JUST IMAGINE THERE'S A HOSEPIPE COMING OUT OF THE BACK OF THE EYE, CONNECTING IT TO YOUR MONSTER'S HEAD!

CREATURE FEATURES

LET'S GIVE YOUR TEETH AND EYES A HOME!

I STARTED WITH A VERY SIMPLE OUTLINE FOR THE MONSTER'S HEAD AND DREW A CIRCLE FOR THE EYE AND A BIG MOUTH SHAPE.

I DREW A PUPIL ON THE EYEBALL AND THEN ADDED SOME TEETH IN THE MOUTH. I DREW THEM NARROWER AND CLOSER AT EITHER SIDE OF THE MOUTH TO SHOW THAT THE TEETH CURVE AROUND IN A 'U' SHAPE.

LASTLY, I FILLED IN THE REST OF THE MOUTH - EVERYTHING THAT ISN'T TEETH!

TRY DIFFERENT TYPES OF EYES WITH DIFFERENT TYPES OF TEETH. THERE ARE SO MANY POSSIBILITIES, SO HAVE FUN PLAYING AROUND!

PROFESSOR BRAYN'S MONSTER TIPS!

MANY THINGS WILL AFFECT HOW YOU DESIGN YOUR MONSTER. HERE ARE SOME THINGS TO CONSIDER BEFORE YOU BEGIN.

BIG CHUNKY ROUNDED TEETH AND SIMPLE EYES MAKE YOUR MONSTER LOOK LESS THREATENING.

LOTS OF SHARP TEETH AND WEIRD EYES WILL GIVE YOUR MONSTER THE SCARE-FACTOR!

BUILDING OUR MONSTER:

HMM, IT CAN SEE ME, AND HAS A MOUTH NOW...

We've just learnt to draw eyes and mouths! Let's add those to a monster!

...IS IT JUST ME OR DOES IT LOOK HUNGRY?!

Learn how to draw horns, tails and much more in *The Phoenix*!

here are more PRO DRAWING TIPS just like this, every week in *The Phoenix*!

SPECIAL PREVIEW!

The Phoenix is the home of the AMAZING *Squid Bits*! All-you-can-eat comi

THE PHOENIX — GREAT STORIES EVERY WEEK

TOOTH and CLAW
Academy for Magical Creatures

Geography, with
Mistress Faraway,
the arctic tern.

There's a
world of magic
just over the
horizon!

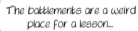

The battlements are a weird
place for a lesson...

Is it
safe?

HA! Safety!

That's for
cowardly
creatures!

To learn the secrets
of magic you must be
Bold Explorers!

Travelling across
faraway lands!

...around the
whole world!

Seeing new mysteries,
amazing sights...
wonders!

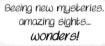

Now,
follow
me...

...and see the territory
the maps can only
hint at...!

Gazing down
on the world
from above!

Do you think
she knows we
can't fly?

....

Read The Phoenix for more MAGIC LESSONS at the Tooth and Claw Academy!

SPECIAL PREVIEW!

Find brand-new SHORTS and hilarious comics in *The Phoenix*!

Wasn't that AWESOME?! Every issue is 36 PAGES!

TO BE CONTINUED! Every issue of *The Phoenix* features EXCITING new episodes of ongoing stories!

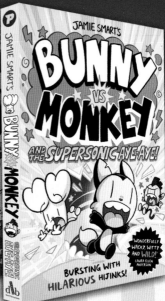
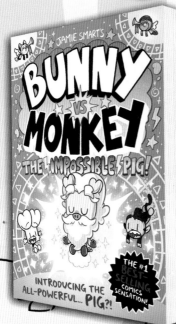

STAR CAT

JAMES TURNER
YASMIN SHEIKH

STAR CAT

SPACE HAS
NEVER BEEN
THIS SILLY

dfb
David Fickling Books

STAR CAT · JAMES TURNER · YASMIN SHEIKH

THEPHOENIXCOMIC.SHOP

MEGA ROBO BROS
THE SERIES

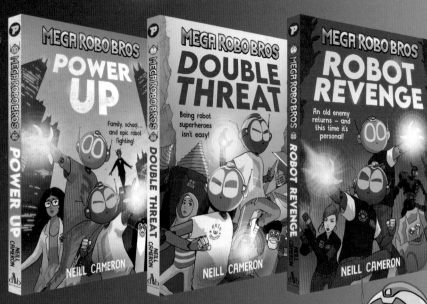

POWER UP
Family, school... and epic robot fighting!

DOUBLE THREAT
Being robot superheroes isn't easy!

ROBOT REVENGE
An old enemy returns – and this time it's personal!

NEILL CAMERON

BROTHERS.
ROBOTS.
SUPERHEROES.

Alex and Freddy are two normal bickering brothers – who also happen to be **super-powered robots!** They're off on school trips, or annoying each other in the playground. But when **robot attacks** take place, [ti]me for the boys to step up!

ABOUT THE AUTHOR

LAURA ELLEN ANDERSON is the bestselling
author/illustrator of the hugely popular *Amelia Fang*
and *Rainbow Grey* illustrated fiction series. She is also
the creator of the popular *I Don't Want...* picture books.

Laura spends every waking hour creating and drawing,
and would quite like to live on the Moon when humans
finally make it possible.